4 *Above* each note write a *higher* note to form the named *harmonic* interval, as shown first answer. The key is B♭ major.

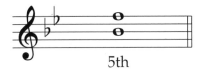

5th

8th/8ve

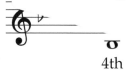

4th

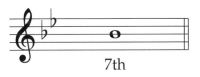

7th

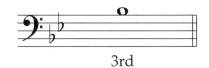

3rd

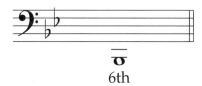

6th

5 Add the correct rest(s) at the places marked ✱ in these two melodies to make each bar complete.

10

Blow

Bizet

6 (a) Rewrite these treble clef notes in the bass clef, keeping the pitch the same. The first answer is given.

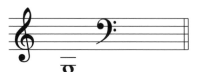

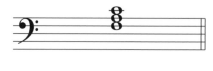

(b) In which major key are all these notes found?   ....

7 Name the keys of these tonic triads.

....

....

4

8 Look at this melody by Scharwenka and then answer the questions below.

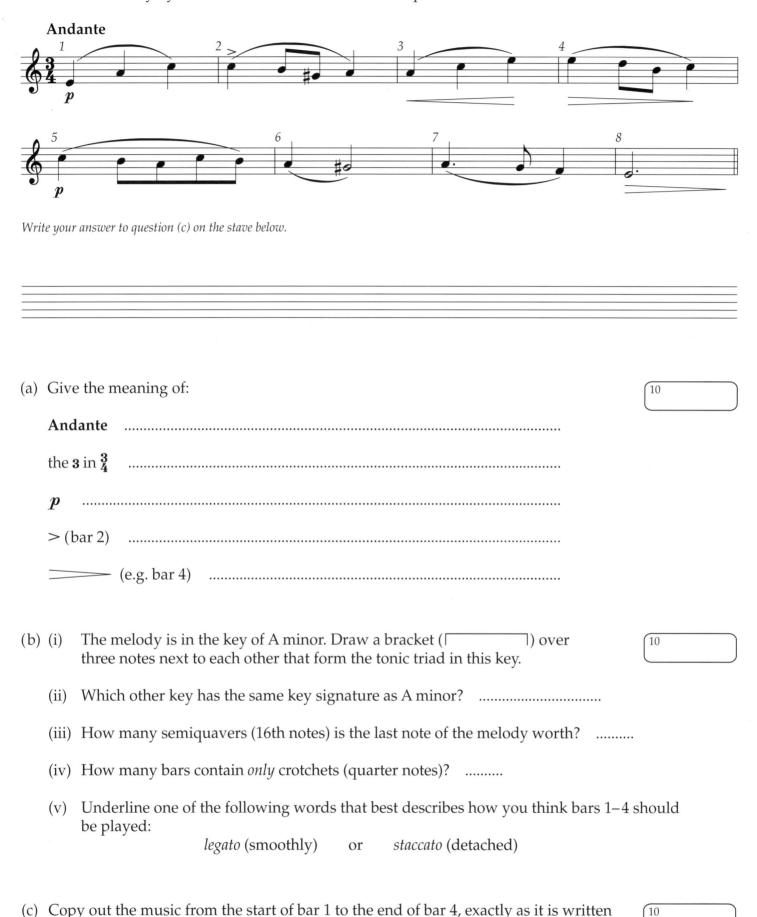

Write your answer to question (c) on the stave below.

(a) Give the meaning of:

10

Andante ....

the **3** in **¾** ....

p ....

> (bar 2) ....

⟍⟋ (e.g. bar 4) ....

(b) (i) The melody is in the key of A minor. Draw a bracket (⌐‾‾‾‾‾¬) over three notes next to each other that form the tonic triad in this key.

10

(ii) Which other key has the same key signature as A minor? ....

(iii) How many semiquavers (16th notes) is the last note of the melody worth? ....

(iv) How many bars contain *only* crotchets (quarter notes)? ....

(v) Underline one of the following words that best describes how you think bars 1–4 should be played:

  legato (smoothly)   or   *staccato* (detached)

(c) Copy out the music from the start of bar 1 to the end of bar 4, exactly as it is written above. Don't forget the clef, time signature, tempo marking, dynamics and all other details. Write the music on the blank stave above question (a). (Marks will be given for neatness and accuracy.)

10

Theory Paper   Grade 2   2015   B

TOTAL MARKS
100

Duration 1½ hours

Candidates should answer ALL questions.
Write your answers on this paper – no others will be accepted.
Answers must be written clearly and neatly – otherwise marks may be lost.

1   Add the time signature to each of these five melodies.   10

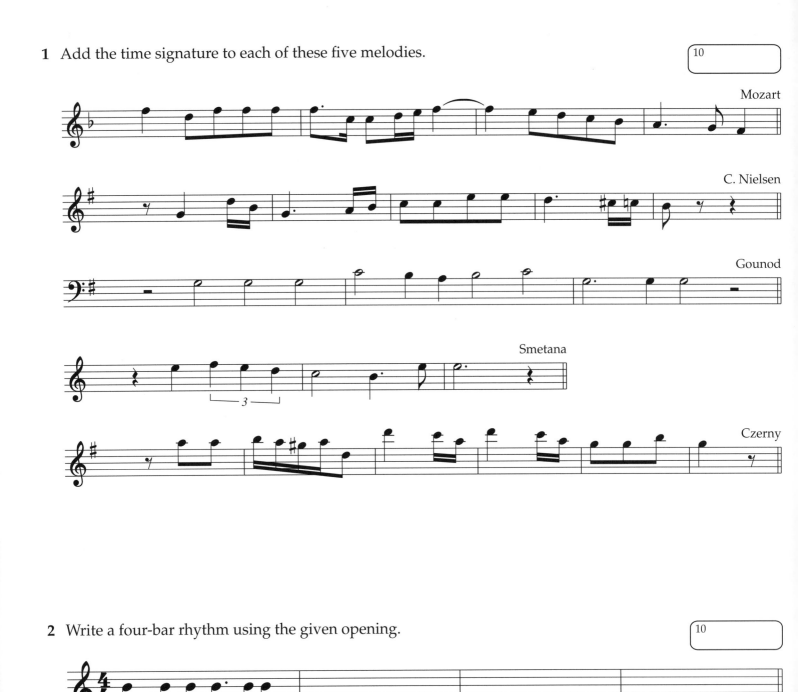

2   Write a four-bar rhythm using the given opening.   10

3 (a) Give the letter name of each of the notes marked ∗, including the sharp sign where necessary. The first answer is given.

A
....

....

(b) Draw a circle around two notes next to each other that are a 5th apart.

4 Rewrite this melody in the treble clef, keeping the pitch the same.
The first three notes are given.

5 Write as semibreves (whole notes) the scales named below.

10

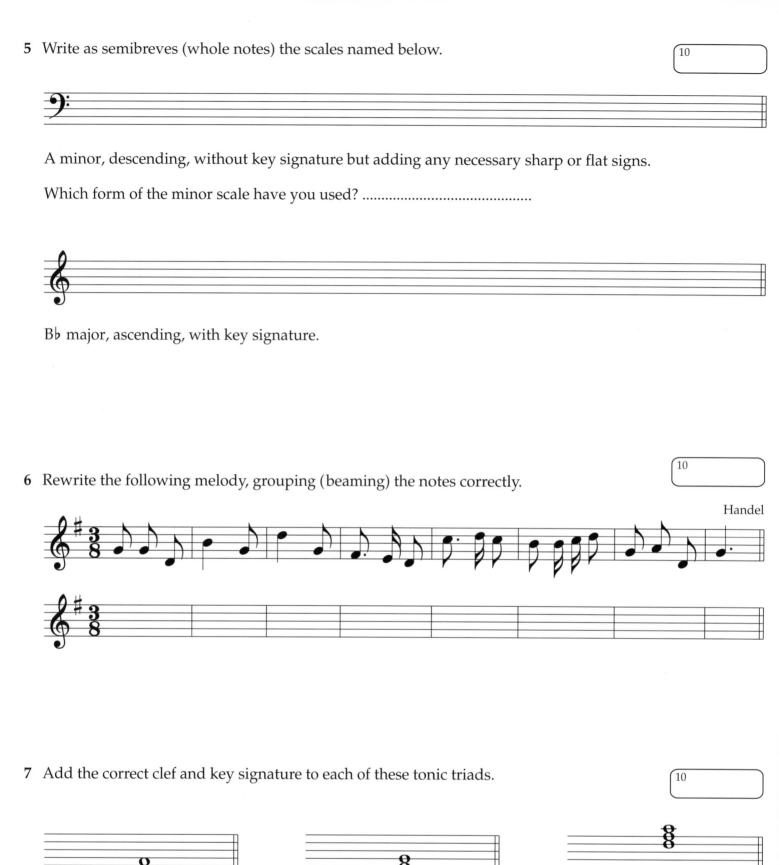

A minor, descending, without key signature but adding any necessary sharp or flat signs.

Which form of the minor scale have you used? ....

B♭ major, ascending, with key signature.

6 Rewrite the following melody, grouping (beaming) the notes correctly.

10

Handel

7 Add the correct clef and key signature to each of these tonic triads.

10

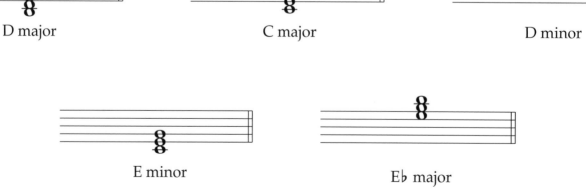

D major

C major

D minor

E minor

E♭ major

8

8 Look at this melody, which is adapted from a piece by Popper, and then answer the questions below.

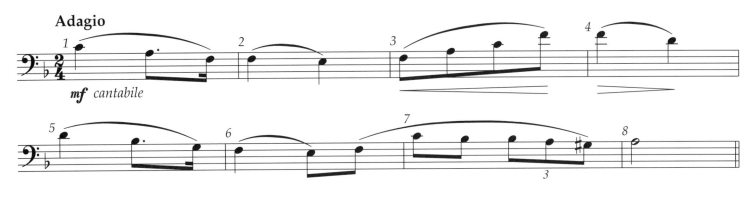

Write your answer to question (c) on the stave below.

(a) Give the meaning of: 〔10〕

Adagio ....

mf ....

cantabile ....

⌢ (e.g. bar 2) ....

◁ (bar 3) ....

(b) (i) The melody is in the key of F major. 〔10〕
Draw a circle around a note that is *not* in this key.

(ii) Give the number of a bar that contains all the notes of the tonic triad of F major. Bar ....

(iii) Complete this sentence:
 The triplet ( ) in bar 7 means three quavers (eighth notes) in the time of ....

(iv) Give the letter name of the *highest* note in the melody. ....

(v) Give the time name (e.g. crotchet or quarter note) of the *longest* note in the melody. ....

(c) Copy out the music from the start of bar 1 to the end of bar 4, exactly as it is written 〔10〕
above. Don't forget the clef, key signature, time signature, tempo marking, dynamics
and all other details. Write the music on the blank stave above question (a). (Marks
will be given for neatness and accuracy.)

Theory Paper   Grade 2   2015   C

Duration 1½ hours

Candidates should answer ALL questions.
Write your answers on this paper – no others will be accepted.
Answers must be written clearly and neatly – otherwise marks may be lost.

TOTAL MARKS
100

1   Add the missing bar-lines to these two melodies. The first bar-line is given in each.

10

Grieg

Bruch

2   Write a four-bar rhythm using the given opening.

10

3   Write as semibreves (whole notes) the scales named below.

10

E minor, ascending, with key signature.
Which form of the minor scale have you used? ....

F major, descending, without key signature but adding any necessary sharp or flat signs.

4 Rewrite this melody in the bass clef, keeping the pitch the same. The first bar is given.

Haydn

5 Add the correct clef to make each of these named notes, as shown in the first answer.

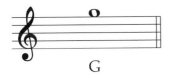

G

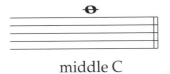

middle C

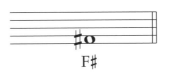

F#

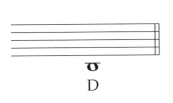

D

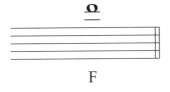

F

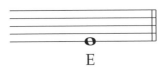

E

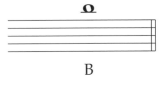

B

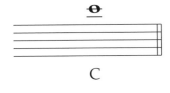

C

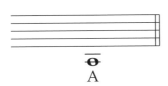

A

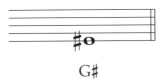

G#

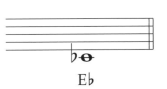

Eb

6 (a) Name the degree of the scale (e.g. 2nd, 3rd) of each of the notes marked ∗, as shown in the first answer. The key is A major. [10]

Mendelssohn

5th ....

(b) How many semiquavers (16th notes) are the
tied notes marked with a bracket (⌐‾‾‾⌐) worth in total?   ....

7 Write the tonic triads named below. Do *not* use key signatures but remember to add any necessary sharp or flat signs. [10]

   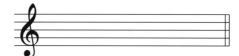   

E♭ major   A minor   D minor

G major   D major

8 Look at this melody by C. Gurlitt and then answer the questions below.

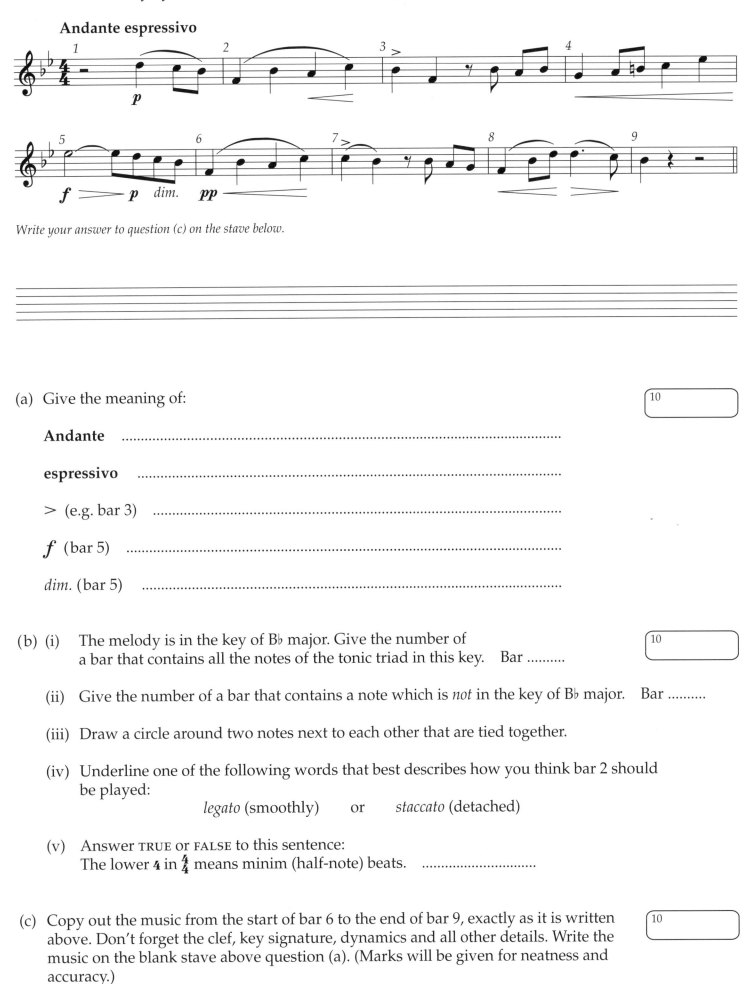

Write your answer to question (c) on the stave below.

(a) Give the meaning of:

Andante ....

espressivo ....

> (e.g. bar 3) ....

f (bar 5) ....

dim. (bar 5) ....

(b) (i) The melody is in the key of B♭ major. Give the number of
a bar that contains all the notes of the tonic triad in this key.   Bar ....

(ii) Give the number of a bar that contains a note which is *not* in the key of B♭ major.   Bar ....

(iii) Draw a circle around two notes next to each other that are tied together.

(iv) Underline one of the following words that best describes how you think bar 2 should
be played:

legato (smoothly)   or   *staccato* (detached)

(v) Answer TRUE or FALSE to this sentence:
The lower **4** in **4/4** means minim (half-note) beats.   ....

(c) Copy out the music from the start of bar 6 to the end of bar 9, exactly as it is written
above. Don't forget the clef, key signature, dynamics and all other details. Write the
music on the blank stave above question (a). (Marks will be given for neatness and
accuracy.)

10

10

10

Theory Paper   Grade 2   2015   S

TOTAL MARKS
100

Duration 1½ hours

Candidates should answer ALL questions.
Write your answers on this paper – no others will be accepted.
Answers must be written clearly and neatly – otherwise marks may be lost.

1 Add the time signature to each of these five melodies.

10

2 Write a four-bar rhythm using the given opening.

10

3 Rewrite the following melody in notes and a rest of *half* the value, beginning as shown.
Remember to group (beam) the notes correctly where necessary.

10

4 Write the tonic triads named below using the correct key signature for each. [10]

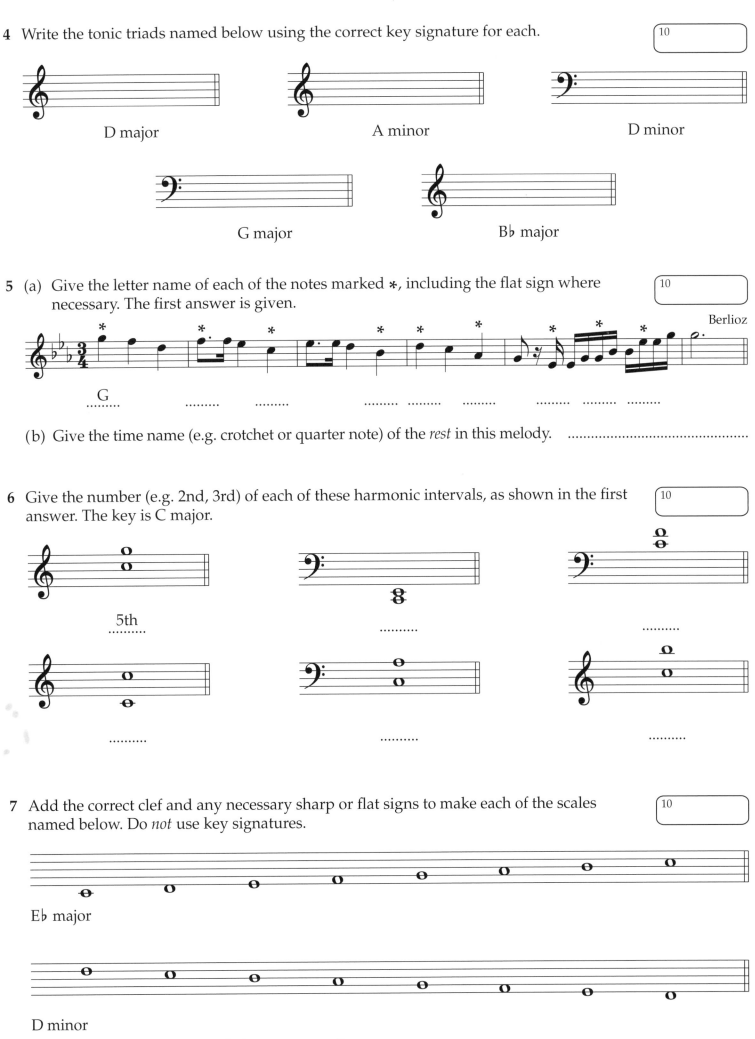

D major

A minor

D minor

G major

Bb major

5 (a) Give the letter name of each of the notes marked *, including the flat sign where necessary. The first answer is given. [10]

Berlioz

G ....

(b) Give the time name (e.g. crotchet or quarter note) of the *rest* in this melody. ....

6 Give the number (e.g. 2nd, 3rd) of each of these harmonic intervals, as shown in the first answer. The key is C major. [10]

5th ....

....

....

....

....

....

7 Add the correct clef and any necessary sharp or flat signs to make each of the scales named below. Do *not* use key signatures. [10]

Eb major

D minor
Which form of the minor scale have you used? ....

8 Look at this folksong melody and then answer the questions below.

Write your answer to question (c) on the stave below.

(a) Give the meaning of:

Allegro ....

moderato ....

♩ = 100 ....

mp ....

the dots above the notes (e.g. bar 5) ....

[10]

(b) (i) The melody is in the key of E minor. Give the number of
a bar that contains all the notes of the tonic triad in this key.   Bar ....

(ii) Give the letter name of the *highest* note in the melody. ....

(iii) Draw a circle around two notes next to each other that are a 5th apart.

(iv) Give the time name (e.g. minim or
half note) of the *longest* note in the melody. ....

(v) Answer TRUE or FALSE to this sentence:
The music gets a little faster in bar 7. ....

[10]

(c) Copy out the music from the start of bar 6 to the end of bar 8, exactly as it is
written above. Don't forget the clef, key signature, dynamics and all other details.
Write the music on the blank stave above question (a). (Marks will be given for
neatness and accuracy.)

[10]

ABRSM
24 Portland Place
London W1B 1LU
United Kingdom

www.abrsm.org

MIX
Paper from
responsible sources
FSC™ C109619

Published by ABRSM (Publishing) Ltd,
a wholly owned subsidiary of ABRSM
Cover by Kate Benjamin & Andy Potts
Printed in England by Halstan & Co. Ltd,
Amersham, Bucks

ISBN 978-1-84849-756-6

9 781848 497566